101 Fun Activities for Retirement:

Your Ultimate Guide to an Exciting, Active, Happy, and Healthy Life after Work

A.J. Johnson

To my wife Meredith, who has brought me joy throughout life, and in our retirement years.

Table of Contents

Free Bonus: Activity Planning Template

ACTIVITY:

WHAT IS YOUR PURPOSE OR OBJECTIVE?

Space to set specific, measurable goals for the activity.
You can then track progress towards these goals.
Are there any specific techniques or skills to focus on?

MOTIVATION AND INSPIRATION:

What inspired you to do this activity?
Do you have an inspiration board? You can add pictures or notes that inspire or relate to the activity.

PLANNING

MATERIALS:

List any necessary items required for the activity.

BUDGET:

Estimate the costs associated with the activity, including equipment, supplies, or any fees.

TIME AVAILABLE:

Determine how often the activity will be pursued (daily, weekly, monthly, etc). Plan the duration of each session or activity session.

ENGAGEMENT:

COMMUNITY:

Note opportunities to engage with others pursuing the same activity, whether in-person or online.

SHARING EXPERIENCES:

Consider avenues for sharing experiences, tips, or insights with others interested in the activity.

MOTIVATIONS AND AFFIRMATIONS:

A space for motivational content to inspire continued engagement in the activity.

REFLECTIONS AFTER THE ACTIVITY:

INITIAL FEELINGS OF THE EXPERIENCE:

Think back on your feelings and sensations at the beginning of the exercise. Think about your feelings leading up to, during, and following the new activity. Were you nervous, excited, or unsure? Being aware of these feelings will enable you to modify your strategy and control expectations.

CHALLENGES:

List any obstacles or problems you ran into whilst doing the activity. Think back on the parts that were harder than you had anticipated and the lessons you learnt from conquering them. How can you make the activity more fun in the future?

FUTURE ACTIVITIES:

Did the activity aligns with your interests and passions?
How can you focus on activities which lead you to an exciting, active, healthy, and happy life?

Introduction

Congratulations for achieving this significant life milestone! You're about to embark on an interesting, energetic, and healthy journey that will take you beyond the mundane routine of work.

Retirement is about getting ready for a new adventure, not just winding down! Imagine yourself going on active treks in the mornings, spending afternoons on the golf course, or riding your bike along beautiful paths. Enjoy the flexibility to design each day as an invitation for exploration and enjoyment, and embrace the delight of being active.

This is your opportunity to support not only your interests but also your overall health. Take up gardening, tend to colourful flowers, and create fresh vegetables on your own. Take up yoga or meditation outside in the peace of nature to promote mental clarity and physical well-being.

Not to mention the excitement of travelling! Get ready for road vacations, stargazing at night, and exploring hidden jewels across the world. There is a big globe full of fascinating cultures, breath-taking scenery, and life-changing events just waiting to be discovered.

But in the middle of all the fun, don't forget to treasure the little things in life. Savour the sweetness of life's small pleasures, go on leisurely picnics with loved ones, and engage in outdoor culinary excursions.

Your retirement is an empty canvas just begging for your colourful brushwork. Make every moment matter, love every day, and take care of your body and mind.

Here's to an exciting, active, health, and happy life after work!

1. Make your bucket list

As you enter this new phase of life, I want to start by telling you the importance of setting goals and dreaming big. That's why I want you to make a retirement bucket list. A bucket list is a guide to the events and activities that are actually important to us—not merely a compilation of fantasies. Finding the things that actually make us feel alive, joyful, and passionate is the key. A retirement bucket list can serve as a roadmap, an ongoing reminder to pursue the activities that bring us joy and make memories that will last a lifetime. Making the most of this new chapter in your life and accepting life's possibilities are more important than just crossing things off a list.

The activities in this book are based on tried and tested experiences. I've built this list during my retirement, gathered ideas, and even talked to friends and family who've tried and tested list of activities in their retirement. You can be sure that these events are planned to provide fulfilling and interesting retirement experiences. Please take inspiration from this list, modify it to suit your needs, and add your own touches. I can promise you that it's an excellent starting point for your retirement bucket list.

There is something quite special about writing down your retirement bucket list on paper. Choose a peaceful, cosy area, take out your trusted pen, and grab a sheet of paper or your beloved notebook. Another option is, if you're more tech-savvy, creating an electronic bucket list on your phone or computer. Adapting it to suit your needs is the key here.

Chapter 1: Explore the Outdoors

Making the most of this stage of life calls for spending time outside. Nature has this amazing power to uplift our bodies, soothe our thoughts, and restore our souls. It provides us with a sense of calm and peace that is difficult to obtain elsewhere. Engaging in activities such as strolling, gardening, hiking, or just relaxing in a park, the outdoors provide us with an opportunity to re-establish a connection with ourselves and the surrounding environment. Getting in touch with nature can make us feel fulfilled, amazed, and appreciative of the beauty all around us. So, allow nature to accompany and assist you on this amazing journey.

2. Go on a hiking adventure

Hiking is an experience that can have a major beneficial effect on your wellbeing, not only a physical activity. It gives you the chance to fully appreciate the beauty of nature, which promotes peace of mind, a connection to the natural world, and a break from daily routine. A sense of renewal and energy is heightened by the physical activity, beautiful scenery, and clean air. Hiking also presents an opportunity to travel to new locations, unearth hidden treasures, and make lifelong memories.

Here's a rundown of key things you might need:

- The right footwear is essential. Make an investment in a decent pair of hiking boots or robust trail shoes that provide comfort and ankle support.
- Clothes: Wear layers that are appropriate for the weather, and carry a waterproof jacket in case!
- Backpack: To carry water, snacks, a first aid kit, a map, and any other necessities you might need, you'll need a comfortable backpack.
- Navigational aids: To make sure you stay on course, carry a map of the route or make use of a GPS unit or smartphone app.
- Water and foods: Drink lots of water to stay hydrated, and carry with you energy-boosting foods like granola bars, trail mix, or almonds.
- Personal Essentials: It's usually a good idea to keep some cash, identification, and a fully charged phone close to hand.

These are a few stunning locations worldwide that provide amazing hiking experiences:

- Grand Canyon, USA: Discover the untamed splendour of one of the most well-known natural wonders on earth. Hiking the canyon paths provides breath-taking views, a rich understanding of the earth's geological past, and a variety of sceneries.
- The Haute Route, France, Switzerland: Hikers can see some of the most stunning scenery in the Alps on this traditional high-level route, which passes through glaciers, quaint towns, and beautiful vistas.
- Tongariro Alpine Crossing, New Zealand: Explore this UNESCO World Heritage site by trekking over stunning volcanic terrain, past green lakes, boiling vents, and bright sceneries.
- The Dolomites, Italy: These are a hiker's paradise, offering a network of paths suitable for all ability levels and featuring stunning views and craggy peaks.
- The Inca Trail, Peru: Travel over lofty mountain passes, cloud forests, and historic ruins to reach the magnificent Machu Picchu. This well-known trek offers gorgeous scenery, history, and a fulfilling sense of achievement.
- Tour du Mont Blanc, France, Italy, Switzerland: This trail offers an amazing trek through alpine meadows, quaint villages, and beautiful mountain vistas as it encircles Mont Blanc, the highest summit in Europe.

- Torres del Paine National Park, Chile: This is well-known for its gob-smacking granite peaks, glaciers, and glistening lakes. It also has a variety of hiking trails, such as the well-known W Trek and the more difficult Circuit Trek.

3. Gardening

Beyond only caring for plants, gardening is a very gratifying and relaxing activity. Taking care of a garden provides peaceful moments, a feeling of achievement, and a special bond with the natural world. This activity offers a chance for both physical exercise and mental renewal in addition to promoting relaxation and lowering tension. The happiness and satisfaction that come from raising life in the splendour of nature, whether it is by tending to a tiny garden or potted plants, may really make this exciting stage of retirement even more enjoyable.

For those who are just starting out, here are some simple yet satisfying gardening ideas:

- Grow Your Own Salad: Sow salad greens such as rocket, spinach or lettuce to start a small food garden. You can pick these lush greens straight from your yard and use them in fresh salads. They are also quite easy to grow.
- Cacti and succulents: Take into consideration cultivating cacti and succulents outdoors in little pots or indoors. They may bring a little greenery into any area, are hardy, and require little watering.
- Planting Seeds: Try your hand at growing simple veggies like beans, peas, or radishes by simply sowing their seeds in your yard. For novice

gardeners, these seeds frequently sprout rather quickly, giving them a sense of success.

- Potted plants or container gardens are a good place to start with gardening. Choose plants that do well in pots, such as flowers, herbs, and cherry tomatoes. They're small enough to fit on balconies, patios, or even windowsills, and they take up less room.
- Herb Garden: Grow simple herbs like parsley, basil, mint, or thyme in a little herb garden. They are satisfying to use in cooking and can be grown in little pots or a special spot in your garden.
- Low-Maintenance Flower Bed: Plant low-maintenance flowers like marigolds, pansies, or zinnias in a compact flower garden. These plants are excellent for adding colour to your yard and typically require less care.

4. Golfing

Golf is more than just hitting balls with clubs; it's a new realm of fun and relaxation. Imagine the tranquil greenery, the soft wind, and the delightful "thwack" of the ball. Golf has a unique way of blending social relaxation with physical exercise. It's more important to enjoy the game, the company, and the relaxed pace than it is to be an expert. It's also a fantastic chance to meet new people, get some vitamin D, and keep active. Take a shot at it—pun intended!

Here are some pointers for the simplest approach to begin golfing:

- Take Lessons: Look for nearby golf clubs or golf instructors who offer beginner or retiree-specific instruction. You may avoid poor habits and save time by learning the fundamentals right from the start with the assistance of a professional.
- Commence with the Fundamentals: Start by paying close attention to the basics: grip, stance, posture, and swing. Prior to moving on to longer strokes, improve your putting and chipping techniques. Regular practise helps to develop muscle memory.
- Use Equipment Suitable for Beginners: Invest in clubs that are easy to use and suitable for beginners. Consistently hitting the ball can be facilitated by clubs with higher lofts and wider clubfaces, such as cavity-back irons.

- Play at Your Own Pace: You have plenty of free time now that you are retired. Benefit from it by practising and performing at a leisurely pace. Take your time studying and developing; don't rush it.
- Play Nine Holes: Rather than playing an entire 18-hole round at first, start with shorter rounds of nine holes. This can help you enjoy the game without feeling tired while increasing your stamina and focus.

5. Fishing

It's about the whole experience, not just about landing the big one (though that is very thrilling). Imagine the peace and quiet of being on the water, surrounded by the splendour of nature, and hearing nothing except the sound of the odd splash and gentle waves. It's a great opportunity to escape the stress of the working world and re-establish a connection with the natural world. A valuable catch can be lured in with patience and technique, which is quite satisfying. The peace and happiness that come from being outside make every moment worthwhile, even on the days when the fish aren't biting.

Some fish species are often seen to be simpler for novices to catch because of their habits, behaviour, and eating patterns. Here are few instances:

- Bluegill/ Sunfish
- Trout
- Catfish
- Crappie
- Pike

6. Outdoor photography

Capturing the amazing grandeur of nature, landscapes, wildlife, and all in between may be accomplished through the thrilling medium of outdoor photography. It's a form of art that lets you use a camera to express your creativity while exploring the great outdoors. Capturing a moment in time, be it a colourful sunrise painting the sky or a beautiful mountain range towering over the horizon, is the essence of outdoor photography's beauty. Seeing the world through a different lens, framing vistas, tracking wildlife behaviours, and learning about the nuances of nature are all important aspects of photography.

Learn the fundamentals of photography before venturing into the world of outdoor photography. Learn how to use the functions and settings of your camera. Try experimenting with the rule of thirds, composition, and framing to produce images that are visually pleasing. Understanding how natural light interacts with your subjects at different times of the day is important for outdoor photography. If your camera would allow it, think about getting a multipurpose lens good for taking pictures of wildlife and landscapes. Above all, practise frequently and have self-compassion. Take advantage of any chance you get to capture the spirit of nature with your camera, as its beauty is immense and always evolving.

7. Outdoor yoga and meditation

Engaging in outdoor yoga and meditation may be a deeply calming and revitalising experience that fosters a connection with the natural world while promoting mindfulness and relaxation. Imagine being surrounded by the soothing sounds of a babbling brook, the warmth of the sun, or the soft rustle of leaves. The health advantages of being in nature combine with the benefits of yoga practise to create outdoor yoga. It's about locating your centre, establishing your grounding, and aligning your motions with the surrounding natural forces.

Spending time in nature during meditation enhances the experience by enabling complete present-moment awareness. Outdoor meditation provides a tranquil setting to calm the mind, relieve tension, and strengthen your connection with the environment, whether you're sitting by a placid lake or atop a serene mountain. Incorporating the sights, sounds, and sensations of nature into your practise helps you relax and cultivate inner peace and harmony.

Look for a quiet area in the outdoors, such as a park, beach, clearing in the forest, or even your backyard, to attempt outdoor yoga and meditation. Place a mat down or just take a comfortable seat. Take part in your regular yoga programme or try mindfulness meditation and deep breathing techniques. Allow the serenity of nature to lead you to inner peace and harmony.

8. Volunteering to help the environment

There are several advantages to volunteering for environmental causes, both for the environment and the volunteer:

Advantages for the Individual

- Sense of Fulfilment: Participating in volunteer work related to environmental issues can provide one a strong sense of purpose and fulfilment. Being aware of how your actions benefit the environment can increase pleasure and self-worth.
- Physical and Mental Health: Both physical and mental health can benefit from volunteering outside. Participating in projects like trail maintenance, beach clean-ups, and tree planting encourages physical activity and lowers stress levels.
- Community and Social Connections: Working with like-minded people while volunteering can help create a feeling of community and help you make important social connections. It offers the chance to socialise with new people and make enduring friendships.

Advantages for the ecosystem

- Volunteers are essential to the preservation and rehabilitation of natural environments. Ecosystem preservation and restoration are directly aided by actions such as clearing contaminated areas, eliminating invasive species, and planting trees.

- Environmental Education: You may spread awareness of environmental issues by volunteering. Volunteers have the power to spread knowledge about sustainable living, conservation techniques, and the value of preserving natural resources.
- Community Involvement: Green volunteer programmes frequently involve the local community in environmental stewardship. This involvement can encourage a sense of responsibility towards the environment and lead to more sustainable practises at the local level.

9. Picnics

The idea of a picnic has been around for centuries, and it has changed over that period due to historical, social, and cultural influences. Derived from the French word "pique-nique," which originally denoted a social gathering where attendees each gave a share of the food, the term "picnic" itself dates back to the 17th century.

The ideal foods to pack for a picnic are those that are portable, can be made ahead of time, and taste good outside. The following is a list of food that are perfect for picnics:

- Sandwiches/ wraps
- Fruit
- Cold cuts
- Crisps
- Drinks

10. Cycling

For many reasons, cycling is a terrific retirement sport. It has many physical, psychological, and social advantages that can make this stage of life much more enjoyable.

Some of the benefits are:

- Physical Fitness: Cycling is a great cardiovascular workout that is low-impact and easy on the joints. It promotes a healthier lifestyle by strengthening muscles, increasing flexibility, and raising general fitness levels.
- Adventure and discovery: Riding a bicycle is the ideal way to discover new locations, be it through picturesque rural routes, coastal pathways, or urban pathways. It enables retirees to experience the freedom of the open road, take in the beauty of nature, and discover new places.
- Stress Reduction and Mental Well-Being: Bicycling outside can help to improve mood, lower stress levels, and quiet the mind. With every ride, it increases endorphins, fosters mental clarity, and gives a feeling of accomplishment.
- Social Interaction: Whether you bike with friends and family, join a group ride, or join a cycling club, cycling may be a social activity. It provides an opportunity to network, form relationships, and exchange experiences, promoting a feeling of community and togetherness.

Developing a greater passion for riding after retirement can be an interesting adventure. The following advice will help you become more enthusiastic and turn riding into a rewarding hobby:

- Set Aims: Decide on specific, attainable objectives that suit your interests and degree of fitness. It can be riding in bicycle races, logging more miles, or finishing a particular trail. Setting and achieving goals provides direction and inspiration to keep riding.
- Route Variability: Discover new bicycle routes to keep things interesting and novel. Alternate between city pathways, rural trails, seaside routes, and mountain bike trails to mix up your trips. A sense of adventure is added and boredom is avoided with variety.
- Join Clubs or Groups for Cycling: Think about joining clubs or groups for area cyclists. Being a part of a cycling community can greatly increase enthusiasm since it offers possibilities for group rides, socialising, and experience sharing, in addition to support.

11. Birdwatching

Birdwatching offers a holistic experience while deepening one's connection to nature and the environment.

The following actions can help spark your interest in birdwatching:

- Start with Observation: Whether you're taking walks, seeing the birds in your neighbourhood park, or your garden, start by keeping an eye on them. Observe their hues, dimensions, actions, and noises. Observe how they engage with the surroundings.
- Learn for Yourself: Go through bird-related books, articles, or movies. Find out about their habitats, migration routes, and behaviours. Birdwatching gets more exciting and rewarding the more you learn.
- Record Sightings: Keep a notebook or logbook in which you can record the species, date, location, and any noteworthy behaviours you see while you see birds. Recording your sightings might be a fulfilling way to monitor your advancement.

Remember, birdwatching should be done ethically by showing respect for the environment and species. Steer clear of upsetting birds, especially in delicate or breeding seasons. Refrain from approaching nests or nesting places too closely and observe from a distance.

Chapter 2: Build creative hobbies

Consider engaging in creatively stimulating hobbies as you approach retirement. In addition to providing a sense of fulfilment, pursuing creative endeavours opens doors to novel experiences and chances for personal development. Creative activities, such as painting, writing, crafts, or learning an instrument, let you discover hidden talents and find new ways to express yourself. These exercises help you develop your creativity, sharpen your problem-solving abilities, and provide you a healthy way to express yourself. Retirement is a great time to take up creative hobbies since they bring excitement and delight to your daily routine, foster a sense of accomplishment, and open doors to new passions and untapped potential.

12. Painting

Painting is a remarkable experience that allows you to create a world of colours, shapes, and emotions out of a blank canvas. Imagine yourself starting an adventure as a storyteller, with a paintbrush full of brilliant colours, and touching it to a blank canvas. It's a kind of self-expression in which you use colour, brushstrokes, and texture to bring your ideas, emotions, and imagination to life.

There's this feeling of wonder and interest when you first start, like you're venturing into unknown terrain. You are free to produce anything you want because you are not constrained by guidelines or restrictions. It all comes down to applying your individual viewpoint to the canvas, whether that takes the form of layers of paint imparting depth and texture or a splatter of bright colours or soft brushstrokes shaping shapes.

Don't stress over having a set plan or being flawless. Painting is about exploration, experimentation, and allowing your imagination to run wild. It's a conversation between your inner self and the canvas, with each brushstroke expressing a thought, a narrative, or an emotion. It's a voyage of self-discovery that can be serene at times or turbulent at others, but it's always an opportunity to express yourself openly and honestly.

Recall that painting has no right or incorrect method. You own the canvas, the colours, and the world. Accept the excitement of discovery, relish the procedure, and allow your creativity to lead the way on this amazing creative journey!

13. Photography

Photography is similar to freezing moments in time into pictures that may convey a lot without using words. Through this art form, you can convey tales, emote, and share your distinct viewpoint with the world. Picture yourself grasping a camera, focusing on a scene through the lens, and then pressing the shutter once to capture a moment in time that will never fade.

Fundamentally, photography is about seeing your surroundings from a different perspective. It's about picking up on subtleties that could otherwise go missed, such as the transient expressions, vivid colours, delicate light and shadow effects, and precise details. You are crafting a story with each photo, deciding what belongs in the frame and what doesn't, and sharing your unique perspective on a subject or a situation.

Taking pictures is like embarking on a journey where you discover new locations, look for undiscovered beauty, and draw inspiration from ordinary scenes. It's an endeavour that tests your ability to observe things from all angles, try out various methods, and develop as an artist over time.

Moreover, photography is about more than just shooting images—it's about arousing feelings and fostering relationships. People who see your photos may feel happy, nostalgic, curious, or in amazement. It's a way for you to express your passions, experiences, and worldview while creating a lasting visual legacy that you and others will treasure.

14. Cooking

Getting involved in cooking as a retiree can be a fulfilling and enjoyable endeavor.

The following five culinary tips which are relevant whether you are a novice or seasoned cook:

1. The secret to cooking successfully is preparation. Make sure you have all the items measured, cut, and ready to use before you begin. No matter how complicated the meal is, this preparation labour, called mise en place, makes the cooking process go more smoothly and efficiently.
2. Taste as You Proceed: Taste your dish frequently while it's cooking. Throughout the cooking process, adjust the flavours, spices, and seasonings as necessary. This guarantees a final result that is well-balanced and lets you adjust the dish to your preference.
3. Use Recipes as a Guide: Although recipes can be useful, don't be scared to stray from them or add your own twist based on your tastes or what ingredients you have on hand. Recipes are only suggestions; feel free to modify them or use different ingredients to suit your preferences.
4. Timing and Patience Are Important: Cooking frequently calls for patience. Give some procedures, like as marinating or simmering, enough time to allow flavours to emerge. For the

best results, pay attention to the temperatures and cooking periods.

5. As You Cook, Keep It Clean: As you go, clean your workplace to keep it organised. While the food is cooking, clean the worktops, cutlery, and dishes. It lessens the amount of cleanup required once the meal is prepared and avoids a disorderly kitchen.

15. Knitting

Using yarn and knitting needles to create fabric or clothing, knitting is a creative and meditative art. Despite being frequently linked to stereotypically feminine pastimes, knitting is a skill that is enjoyed by all genders! Consider employing needles to create elaborate designs, blankets, hats, scarves, and more out of yarn.

There are just two things you'll need to begin knitting:

- Knitting needles: Usually constructed of plastic, bamboo, or metal, they come in a variety of sizes and varieties. The thickness and length of the needles vary based on the type of project you're working on and the weight of the yarn.
- Yarn: Pick the right yarn for the task at hand. Yarns are made of various materials (such as wool, cotton, acrylic, etc.) and weights (thickness). Medium-weight yarn may be easier for beginners to work with.

There are a number of great materials available to help you learn how to knit:

- Local Craft businesses and Yarn Shops: A lot of local craft businesses and yarn shops provide beginning knitting classes. Teachers frequently offer practical direction, advice, and encouragement as you master the fundamentals.

- Online instructions and Videos: There are a plenty of knitting instructions and videos available for beginners on websites like YouTube. You can find demonstrations, advice, and step-by-step instructions for a variety of knitting techniques on knitting-specific channels.
- Knitting Books and Guides: A plethora of books and guides are available that are tailored especially for novice knitters. Seek out knitting books for beginners that outline methods, include patterns, and provide advice on how to fix problems.

16. Writing

You can express yourself artistically through writing. Whether through essays, poetry, journaling, or storytelling, it provides a vehicle for expressing ideas, feelings, and thoughts. Writing stimulates creativity and inquiry. Through your words, you can conjure up whole worlds, casts of characters, or situations, delving into fantastical worlds and discovering countless possibilities.

Your imagination has an open canvas when you write. You are not limited in your ability to develop worlds, characters, or stories. Exploration and enjoyable experimentation are made possible by this creative freedom. You can explore a wide range of ideas, concepts, and scenarios through writing. Exploring many themes and genres, regardless of one's preference for fantasy, mystery, romance, or non-fiction, keeps the writing process lively and engaging.

17. Paper Crafts

Paper crafts are a broad category of crafts that involve the manipulation, production, and transformation of objects made mostly out of paper. These crafts are adaptable, enabling a wide range of creative expressions and useful creations. These are a few popular categories of paper crafts:

- Scrapbooking
- Card Making
- Origami
- Papercutting
- Paper Collage

18. Home decorating

The goal of home decorating is to improve and decorate a house's interior areas to create a cosy, useful, and visually beautiful setting. It's the process of making changes to a living area so that it reflects the homeowner's tastes, style, and personality while still being functional.

Important components of interior design include:

- Lighting
- Decorative elements
- Furniture arrangement
- Painting

19. Learning a new instrument

Depending on personal tastes, passions, and innate tendencies, learning a musical instrument might be difficult or easy. However, because of their low learning curves and easy approaches, certain instruments are typically seen as being easier for beginners. These are a handful:

- Ukulele: The ukulele is renowned for its compact size, four strings on average, and comparatively straightforward chord structures. Compared to the steel strings on guitars, its nylon strings are kinder to the fingertips.
- Piano/Keyboard: The piano provides a visual arrangement of keys and notes, which facilitates the understanding of musical concepts by novices. Simple chords and melodies are easy to pick up fast.
- Recorder/Flute: Because of their simple fingering systems, entry-level flutes and the recorder make it simpler for novices to generate basic notes and melodies.

20. Pottery

Even if you've never tried pottery before, giving it a try may be a fun and fulfilling experience. Locate a community centre or pottery studio in your area that offers introductory courses or classes. Professional instructors who walk you through the fundamentals of handling clay, shaping forms, and utilising pottery tools are frequently available in these programmes. Accept the tactile sensation of shaping clay with your hands and pick up different skills like hand-building or utilising a pottery wheel. Don't be scared to try new things and get your hands dirty! Your initial ceramic creations will be assisted by the instructor as they introduce you to basic techniques.

Recall that enjoying the process and accepting the learning curve are key. So embrace the mess, get started, and let your creativity run wild as you go off on this rewarding adventure into the world of pottery!

21. Dance

Regardless of your prior experience, learning to dance can be an exciting and joyous endeavour. Look into community centres or nearby dancing studios or gyms that provide beginning-level dance instruction. Seek out beginner-oriented lessons, such as basic courses in ballroom, hip-hop, salsa, and even folk dances. These lessons frequently offer a friendly atmosphere and knowledgeable teachers who clearly explain fundamental rhythms, steps, and motions.

Enjoy the beat, let go of inhibitions, and embrace the music as you pick up basic skills and basic choreography. Recall that dancing is a form of self-expression and enjoyment, so just have fun and move to the beat instead of worrying about being perfect! As you venture into this exciting world for the first time, the encouraging environment of a beginner's class will help you develop your confidence and discover the joy of dance.

Chapter 3. Work on your fitness

Maintaining a high quality of life in retirement requires continuing to be active and making fitness a priority. Consider it an investment in your general health and wellbeing! Frequent exercise improves your strength, flexibility, and endurance, which benefits your physical health, but it also has a positive impact on your emotional well-being. It prevents chronic illnesses, manages weight, and enhances balance, which lowers the chance of falls. Becoming physically healthy also helps you sleep better, feel better emotionally, and have more energy, which lets you enjoy this stage of life to the fullest. Let's lace up our shoes and start this fitness journey together! It's about feeling strong, powerful, and making the most out of every day!

22. Walking

During retirement, walking is an excellent and convenient way to increase general fitness. It's a low-impact workout with lots of health advantages that doesn't require any equipment. Walking on a regular basis can enhance endurance, build muscles, and improve cardiovascular health. It's a useful method for controlling weight, improving joint flexibility, and increasing bone density, all of which lower the risk of osteoporosis. Beyond its physical advantages, walking improves mental health by lowering stress, elevating mood, and strengthening cognitive abilities. Walking is a simple yet effective technique to improve overall fitness and enjoy the many health benefits it offers. You can walk briskly along scenic trails or take leisurely strolls through the neighbourhood.

23. Swimming

Swimming is a fun and healthful exercise that can significantly improve general fitness, especially in retirement. It is a full-body workout that works several muscle groups at once and is low-impact, making it appropriate for a range of fitness levels. Swimming on a daily basis can help to increase flexibility, muscle strength, and cardiovascular endurance. Swimming is also a great alternative for people with arthritis or joint pain because it is easy on the joints. By efficiently burning calories, this aquatic workout helps control weight in addition to toning muscles. Beyond improving physical health, swimming lowers tension and fosters mental relaxation. It also provides a meditative experience as you glide over the water. For those with experience, swimming can be done in open water or both indoors and outdoors.

24. Group fitness classes

Retirement fitness can be maintained in a dynamic and inspiring fashion with group exercise programmes. These group fitness sessions, which accommodate different exercise tastes and fitness levels, are facilitated by certified instructors. All it takes to sign up is to make an inquiry at neighbourhood fitness centres, gyms, or community centres that provide a range of classes including dance, yoga, Pilates, aerobics, or strength training.

Encouraging social contact and accountability in a friendly setting, these group sessions help participants develop a sense of camaraderie. It's a chance to pick the brains of knowledgeable instructors, get pointers on correct form, and maintain motivation with like-minded fitness enthusiasts. These sessions also give workouts a fun and varied element that keeps people interested and dedicated to their fitness regimens. Taking advantage of group exercise sessions after retirement guarantees a well-rounded fitness programme and fosters social interactions, which enhances the enjoyment and efficacy of workouts.

25. Pilates

Joseph Pilates created the physical exercise method known as Pilates at the beginning of the 20th century. Its main goals are to increase body awareness, strength, and flexibility. In order to strengthen the core, increase physical strength, and correct posture, it entails deliberate breathing exercises, controlled movements, and focused attention.

Pilates exercises can be done using specialised equipment such as the Reformer, Cadillac, or Chair (Equipment-based Pilates) or on a mat (Mat Pilates). Mat Pilates focuses on core strength, flexibility, and muscular endurance through a sequence of floor movements that use body weight as resistance. Conversely, spring-loaded equipment is used in equipment-based Pilates to generate resistance, enabling a wider variety of exercises that target different muscle areas at different intensities.

Pilates's mild yet effective style makes it very helpful for senior citizens. It is appropriate for people with joint problems or restricted mobility since it places an emphasis on controlled motions and low-impact exercises. Pilates promotes better posture and lowers the risk of falls by enhancing balance, stability, and flexibility. Its emphasis on core strength helps relieve back discomfort and promotes the health of the spine. Additionally, because Pilates movements can be tailored to each person's needs and skills, older individuals can participate in a flexible and safe fitness programme that improves their general well-being.

26. Personal training

During your retirement years, hiring a personal trainer can be a very wise investment in your fitness quest. A personal trainer is a licenced fitness expert who creates workout programmes specifically suited to your needs, skills, and medical concerns. Investigating nearby gyms, fitness centres, or internet resources that provide personal training services is the first step in finding a personal trainer. There are many advantages to hiring a personal trainer, such as receiving individualised attention and direction about workouts, form, and technique. In order to provide a safe and efficient training regimen, they design structured and diverse workouts that are tailored to your tastes and degree of fitness.

A personal trainer can also be a source of inspiration, providing accountability, support, and encouragement as you progress towards your fitness goals. A personal trainer can create programmes for senior citizens that address their current health concerns and limits and emphasise strengthening, flexibility, balance, and overall mobility. A personal trainer can help retirees reach their fitness objectives, build confidence, and improve their general quality of life with a customised approach.

27. Water aerobics

Exercises combining strength and cardio training are performed in a pool as part of water aerobics, sometimes referred to as aquatic exercise or water fitness. This type of exercise uses water resistance and buoyancy to produce resistance and support the body while working out in shallow or deep water. People can participate in water aerobics by enrolling in classes at community centres, swimming pools, or fitness centres that specialise in aquatic exercise.

Exercises like running, jumping jacks, leg lifts, arm circles, and other aerobic exercises modified for the water are common in water aerobics programmes. Water resistance is a great kind of exercise for older persons, people with joint problems, arthritis, or limited mobility since it works the muscles without being too harsh on the joints.

There are many advantages to this type of exercise for retirees. Water's buoyancy lessens the impact on joints, reducing the chance of injury while yet offering a good workout. Strength, endurance, flexibility, and cardiovascular fitness are all improved by water aerobics. Furthermore, the inherent resistance of the water allows for higher workout intensities without the need for bulky equipment, which promotes better balance and coordination.

Attending water aerobics courses encourages social interaction and creates a fun, encouraging environment for group exercise. Water is also a delightful and comfortable exercise alternative because of its cooling effect, which helps reduce sweating during workouts, especially in hot areas. All things considered, water aerobics is a great way for retirees to stay in shape, enhance their general health, and engage in an enjoyable and productive exercise routine.

28. Stand-up Paddleboarding

In stand-up paddleboarding (SUP), you stand on a big board and move through the water with a paddle. This adaptable water sport is fun in a variety of environments, from calm lakes to coastal waves. Beginners can usually hire the necessary equipment (a paddleboard, paddle, and personal flotation device) from nearby paddleboard rental companies or water sports stores to begin stand-up paddleboarding as a hobby.

Find a shallow, quiet body of water to start with, preferably with few waves and currents. To gain a sense of balance, start off kneeling on the paddleboard and work your way up to standing once you're comfortable. To manoeuvre and glide across the water, hold the paddle appropriately and apply soft strokes on either side of the board.

For a number of reasons, stand-up paddleboarding is particularly advantageous for senior citizens. First of all, it's a low-impact exercise that works the entire body without overstressing joints. Enhancing balance, stability, and core strength are essential for preserving mobility and averting falls as we age. Paddleboarding also provides a calm and serene method to interact with the natural world, lowering stress levels and enhancing mental health. Older people can paddle at their own pace and progressively increase in difficulty because it is adaptive to different skill levels, making it a fun and accessible sport for retirees looking for a different way to be active and connected to the outdoors.

29. Treadmill workouts

Using a motorised device with a moving belt, treadmill exercises imitate running, jogging, or walking indoors. Beginners can acquire a treadmill for use at home or visit nearby gyms and fitness centres to begin a treadmill workout. Before getting onto the belt, it is imperative to acquaint oneself with the machine's controls, safety features, and handrails.

As fitness levels develop, start at a comfortable pace, such a brisk walk, and progressively increase speed or incline. Numerous treadmills come with pre-programmed routines, adjustable speeds, and incline levels so users can tailor their workouts to their own tastes and fitness objectives.

Exercise on a treadmill has various benefits for senior citizens. They offer a regulated and weather-resistant atmosphere, which makes it a secure choice for working out indoors, come rain or shine. Additionally, cushioned surfaces found on treadmills are kinder to joints than outside surfaces, which lowers the possibility of impact-related injuries. Because of this, treadmill workouts are especially beneficial for elderly persons who have arthritis or joint problems. Better tracking of progress and motivation during exercises is also made possible by the machine's display of heart rate, distance, and speed. All things considered, treadmill workouts provide senior citizens with a flexible and easy option to maintain overall fitness, increase endurance, and engage in cardiovascular exercise inside a secure indoor environment.

30. Functional training

Strength, flexibility, balance, and coordination are improved by functional training, which consists of exercises that replicate everyday movements. This improves an individual's capacity to carry out daily tasks more efficiently. To begin functional training, people can work with a qualified personal trainer who is experienced in functional training methods, or they can enrol in fitness classes at nearby gyms or fitness centres that are especially focused on functional exercises.

In order to target many muscle groups at once, functional training regimens frequently include bodyweight exercises, resistance bands, stability balls, medicine balls, kettlebells, and other equipment. In order to mimic practical tasks found in everyday life, the exercises have an emphasis on natural motions including pushing, pulling, squatting, lifting, twisting, and bending.

The practical approach of functional training makes it very effective for older persons. Enhancing total functional fitness lowers the chance of injury, increases independence as people age, and facilitates the performance of daily duties. Functional training improves balance and stability by focusing on muscles utilised in daily activities. These abilities are essential for avoiding falls and preserving mobility. It also helps strengthen the core muscles that support the spine, correct imbalances, and enhance posture.

Furthermore, different fitness levels and abilities can be accommodated through the adaptation of functional training, enabling older adults to begin at a reasonable intensity and work their way up progressively. It's the perfect workout programme for retirees because it emphasises movements that are applicable to everyday life.

31. Plyometric exercises

Plyometric workouts, sometimes referred to as jump training, focus on power, speed, agility, and general athletic performance through explosive movements that apply maximal force in brief bursts. People can begin plyometric workouts at home or in a gym and add them into their training regimens.

Plyometric workouts that are frequently performed include burpees, box jumps, jump squats, bounding, and plyo push-ups. These workouts usually involve quick muscular contractions (concentric phase) that result in a forceful movement after a rapid muscle stretch (eccentric phase). When starting out, beginners should work on correct form and technique with basic exercises before moving on to more complex plyometric actions.

Even while plyometric workouts are frequently connected to sports training, with the right adaptation, they can also be advantageous for senior citizens. Reduced-intensity and low-impact plyometric exercises, including stepping exercises or modified squat jumps, can enhance bone density, muscle strength, and coordination without putting undue strain on joints.

Plyometric exercises can help older persons become more functionally fit, improve their balance, and decrease their risk of falling because they increase stability and agility. Plyometrics should be done carefully and gradually, taking into account each person's current level of fitness as well as any joint or mobility problems. Plyometric workouts can be safe and appropriate for older people looking to improve their general fitness and functional abilities if they speak with a fitness expert or healthcare provider.

Chapter 4: Travel on an Adventure

Embracing travel in retirement can be immensely rewarding and enlightening, especially now that you have the time and leisure to pursue travel Retirement travel provides an unmatched chance to experience different cultures, interact with a wide range of people, and make priceless memories. It's an opportunity to embrace adventure, find fresh interests, and revitalise oneself. Travelling not only gives you a break from your daily routine but also broadens your horizons and promotes personal development by exposing you to new ideas. Every journey turns into a tale, an unwritten chapter of encounters. So grab this chance, gather your belongings, and go out on these amazing journeys that are waiting for you!

In this chapter, I will give you 10 top travel destinations around the world, to check out during your retirement!

32. Savannah, Georgia, USA

There are many experiences in Savannah, Georgia, just waiting to be discovered by visitors. Explore the city's historic quarter first; it is a veritable gold mine of gorgeous buildings, mossy oaks, and charming squares. Enjoy a leisurely stroll down River Street to discover the quaint shops, galleries, and mouthwatering restaurants that lie ahead. Visit sites like Bonaventure Cemetery, the Cathedral of St. John the Baptist, and Forsyth Park to learn about the rich history of the city. Enjoy the dynamic art scene and institutions showcasing the rich cultural legacy of the city.

Enjoy the dynamic art scene and institutions showcasing the rich cultural legacy of the city. Savour Southern cuisine at neighbourhood restaurants and indulge in specialties like shrimp and grits or delectable pralines to fully experience the city's gastronomic offerings.

Finally, take advantage of the well-known Southern hospitality by mingling with the locals, going on a ghost tour, or just unwinding in this charming city's peaceful beauty. Savannah offers visitors a beautiful fusion of charm, history, and friendliness to enjoy and relish.

33. Banff National Park, Canada

Situated amidst the Canadian Rockies, Banff National Park provides visitors with an amazing natural amusement park brimming with breathtaking views and outdoor experiences. Start by discovering the renowned turquoise waters of Lake Louise and Moraine Lake, which are flanked by towering peaks and offer ideal conditions for summertime hiking and canoeing as well as wintertime ice-skating and snowshoeing. Travel the picturesque Icefields Parkway and take in the sights of glaciers, waterfalls, and a variety of wildlife.

Take on thrilling walks for those who love the great outdoors, like those that lead to the Sentinel Pass or the Plain of Six Glaciers, which provide panoramic views of the breathtaking scenery. After a day of exploring, don't pass up the opportunity to unwind in the calming waters of Banff Upper Hot Springs. Discover the lively vibe of Banff, which is home to quaint stores, eateries, and galleries that feature regional artwork. For those who are looking for adventure or peace amidst the splendour of nature, Banff National Park ensures that their stay will be one to remember.

34. Machu Picchu, Peru

Travellers are drawn to Machu Picchu, Peru, a UNESCO World Heritage Site tucked away in the Andes Mountains by its ethereal charm and historic marvels. Explore the magnificent ruins of this old Incan city at the start of your tour and be amazed by its elaborate stone terraces, temples, and breath-taking panoramic views. Choose between hiking the traditional Inca Trail or taking a different path such as the Salkantay or Lares routes, which both provide amazing views and a different viewpoint along the way. Take in the sunrise or sunset over the historic citadel to really embrace the mystical atmosphere of this ancient location.

Don't pass up the chance to explore the bustling markets and local culture of the nearby town of Aguas Calientes. Visit the Machu Picchu Museum to learn about Incan legacy and to experience the fusion of history and culture. Explore the Sacred Valley, which is surrounded by picturesque villages and Incan sites like Ollantaytambo and Pisac, to fully appreciate the magnificence of the area. Amidst the ruins of an ancient civilization, Machu Picchu beckons visitors to set off on a voyage of exploration and adventure with its breathtaking archaeological remains and ethereal beauty.

35. Santorini, Greece

Greece's Santorini, renowned for its breathtaking views, sunsets, and alluring beauty, provides visitors with an utterly enthralling experience. Start by touring the island's recognisable blue-domed churches and white-washed buildings in quaint communities like Oia and Fira. Take in the breathtaking view of the caldera as the sun sets over Oia, a popular destination for sunset watchers. Experience the rich history of the island by touring sites such as Akrotiri, which is sometimes called the "Minoan Pompeii."

Savour the regional fare, which includes mouthwatering Greek delicacies, fresh seafood, and well-known wines, all while taking in views of the Aegean Sea. Unwind on the gorgeous beaches of the island, which offer perfect settings for swimming and sunbathing. From the crimson sands of crimson Beach to the black sands of Perissa. Don't pass up the chance to see the volcanic islands by boat or discover the distinctive wineries and vineyards located all around the island. Discovering the island's rich history, savouring its mouthwatering cuisine, or simply taking in the breathtaking scenery, Santorini beckons visitors to experience the allure of a Greek island unlike any other.

36. Dubrovnik, Croatia

Travellers are drawn to Dubrovnik, Croatia, sometimes referred to as the "Pearl of the Adriatic," by its breathtaking shoreline, rich history, and antique charm. Start your trip by exploring the city's well-preserved mediaeval fortifications, which provide expansive views of the Adriatic Sea and houses with red roofs. Discover the fascinating Old Town, which is recognised as a UNESCO World Heritage Site. You may also see famous historical sites including the Dubrovnik Cathedral, Sponza Palace, and the Rector's Palace. Stroll down the city's main thoroughfare, Stradun, which is adorned with stores, cafes, and historically significant structures.

Don't pass up the opportunity to ride the cable car up Mount Srd, which offers stunning views of the surrounding islands and the city. Explore the local museums and art galleries or catch a show at the Dubrovnik Summer Festival to fully immerse yourself in the local culture. Take a boat ride to the neighbouring Elaphiti Islands for a peaceful getaway, or just kick back and relax on one of the immaculate beaches, including Banje Beach. Savour mouthwatering seafood and traditional Croatian specialties, accompanied by regional wines and spirits. Travellers are invited to step back in time and immerse themselves in an absolutely amazing experience along the Adriatic coast by Dubrovnik's unique blend of history, beauty, and coastal charm.

37. Rome, Italy

Rome, Italy, is a timeless city rich in culture, history, and art that transports visitors to another era. Start your journey by seeing famous sites like the Pantheon, the Roman Forum, and the Colosseum and taking in the magnificent architecture of ancient Rome. Discover the Vatican City, which is the location of St. Peter's Basilica and the Vatican Museums, which are home to magnificent works of art such as the Sistine Chapel, a masterpiece by Michelangelo. Explore the quaint streets, piazzas, and fountains to find hidden gems like the Spanish Steps and the Trevi Fountain. Savour traditional Italian fare at neighbourhood trattorias, including pasta carbonara and delectable gelato.

Take in the lively atmosphere of Rome by exploring the city's diverse culture and stopping by busy markets like Campo de' Fiori. Relax in Rome's stunning gardens and parks, like Villa Borghese, which provide peaceful havens from the bustle of the city. Rome invites visitors to take in the ageless beauty and charm of the eternal city with its wealth of historical landmarks, architectural wonders, and creative legacy.

38. Cape Town, South Africa

South Africa's Cape Town is a mesmerising location that combines active metropolitan life, cultural diversity, and scenic beauty. Start your journey by taking a picturesque walk or the cable car up to the summit of Table Mountain, where you can take in expansive views of the city and coastline. Explore the dramatic landscapes of the Cape Peninsula, which include Boulders Beach's penguin colony and the breathtaking Cape Point. Discover the complicated history of South Africa and see the famous Robben Island, the site of Nelson Mandela's imprisonment. Explore the bustling Bo-Kaap neighbourhood, which is well-known for its brightly coloured homes and rich Cape Malay history.

Discover the vibrant V&A Waterfront, a centre for dining, shopping, and entertainment that offers stunning views of Table Mountain and the harbour. Savour the flavours and wines of South Africa at well-known eateries and wineries in the neighbouring Winelands. Explore the Kirstenbosch National Botanical Garden, which features breathtaking scenery and a wide variety of plants. Don't miss this opportunity. At the southernmost point of Africa, Cape Town provides visitors with a unique and varied experience with its blend of natural beauties, cultural events, and friendly hospitality.

39. Bali, Indonesia

Travellers are captivated by Bali, Indonesia, a tropical paradise rich in spirituality and natural beauty, which combines tranquil scenery, lively culture, and kind people. Explore the verdant rice terraces of Tegallalang or Jatiluwih to start your Bali experience. These locations provide breathtaking panoramic views and an insight into the island's agricultural past. Experience the mysticism of Bali by travelling to hallowed sites such as Uluwatu or Tanah Lot, which are positioned on cliffs with stunning views of the ocean. Explore the creative centre of Ubud, where the island's diversity is on display through traditional dance performances, art galleries, and craft markets.

Savour revitalising spa treatments, participate in yoga retreats, or just unwind on Seminyak, Kuta, or Nusa Dua's immaculate beaches. Don't pass up the chance to dive or snorkel Bali's underwater world at locations like Menjangan Island and Amed, which have colourful coral reefs and a wide variety of marine life. Savour a feast of regional cuisine, ranging from Nasi Goreng to Babi Guling, to fully appreciate the island's culinary charms. Bali's breathtaking scenery, spiritual atmosphere, and cultural events all entice visitors to embrace peace and uncover the island's own appeal.

40. Kyoto, Japan

Kyoto, Japan, provides visitors with an enthralling glimpse into Japan's rich history and customs. Kyoto is renowned for its timeless beauty, cultural heritage, and tranquil surroundings. Visit Kyoto's well-known temples, like Ginkaku-ji (the Silver Pavilion) and Kinkaku-ji (the Golden Pavilion), which are decorated with gorgeous architecture and peaceful gardens, to start your exploration. Stroll through Gion's historic neighbourhood to see the traditional tea houses and specialty shops, and maybe even see a glimpse of a geisha dressed in traditional garb. Discover the charming Arashiyama neighbourhood, known for its historic Tenryu-ji Temple, lovely riverbanks, and bamboo groves.

Experience the serene atmosphere of Fushimi Inari Shrine, renowned for its numerous torii gates that lead to the summit of the mountain. Visit Nishiki Market, where regional artists display their creations together with mouthwatering street cuisine, to learn about the skill of traditional crafting. Savour Kyoto's elegant food offerings, such as kaiseki dishes and matcha-flavored pastries, to fully appreciate the creativity and tastes of Japanese cuisine. Kyoto welcomes visitors to fully immerse themselves in the grace and elegance of old Japan with its tranquil temples, charming historic district, and diverse cultural offerings.

41. Sydney, Australia

Travellers may experience a blend of famous sites, gorgeous beaches, and a bustling cultural scene in Sydney, Australia, a lively metropolis situated amid breathtaking natural environments. Visit the famous Sydney Opera House and Sydney Harbour Bridge first as these iconic representations of the city's beauty and architectural grandeur will kick off your exploration of Sydney. Saunter down Bondi Beach's, Bronte's, or Manly's picturesque coastline and take in the sun, waves, and beachside eateries. Discover The Rocks, a historic neighbourhood with bustling markets, art galleries, and cobblestone streets.

Savour fresh seafood at Sydney's renowned fish markets or embrace the city's cultural variety and culinary delights in Chinatown's busy markets. Discover peace in the middle of nature at the Royal Botanic Garden, which has a plethora of flora and stunning views of the harbour. Visit galleries, museums, and the Sydney Opera House to get a taste of the dynamic cultural culture in the city. The opportunity to see expansive views of the city's cityscape from a ferry journey across Sydney Harbour should not be missed. Sydney provides visitors with a fascinating and varied experience down under with its blend of metropolitan attractions, scenic beauty, and lively culture.

Chapter 5: Build social networks

A group of people linked by common interests or different platforms is called a social network. Developing a social network becomes crucial as you approach retirement for a number of reasons. Through connections with others who have similar interests, pastimes, or career backgrounds, these networks provide a means of building supportive networks and deep relationships.

In retirement, establishing a social network is essential for a number of reasons:

- Intellectual Stimulation: Having discussions and doing activities with other people opens the mind, promotes learning, and fosters personal development.
- Mental Well-Being: Social ties help people feel less alone and isolated, which lowers stress and improves mental health.
- Emotional Support: Having a network gives you a sense of connection, belonging, and emotional support.
- Physical Health: Research indicates that having social ties promotes greater physical health, which in turn promotes lifespan and general well-being.

42. Neighbourhood activities

Participating in local events is a great way to foster a feeling of neighbourhood and create deep relationships with neighbours. Start by planning or taking part in neighbourhood gatherings such as potlucks, block parties, or clean-up days. In addition to helping your community, becoming a member of your neighbourhood watch or homeowners' association gives you the chance to interact and work together with your neighbours. One of the best ways to meet people in the area is to participate in neighbourhood activities like garage sales, holiday festivities, gardening organisations, or walking groups.

43. Join a gym or fitness class

Enrolling in fitness courses or joining a gym is a great way to improve your physical health while also meeting new people and growing your social network. Group exercise programmes like yoga, Pilates, Zumba, or spinning are frequently offered by gyms, offering a friendly setting for people who value wellbeing and health to connect. Working out in a group promotes friendship and provides chances to socialise in a safe environment. Participating in the gym's physical challenges or programmes can also help to promote social contact and collaboration. Before or after courses, conversations may get really going, which helps you connect with other members over common fitness objectives and experiences.

44. Attend cultural events

Participating in cultural events is a rewarding way to meet others who are passionate about art, music, and cultural heritage and to immerse oneself in a variety of experiences. These gathering places, which might include festivals, theatre plays, music concerts, and art exhibits, give people a chance to interact with one another and pursue common interests. They provide an opportunity to interact with individuals from other origins, encouraging conversations and relationships based on a shared love of cultural manifestations. Cultural events frequently include interactive sessions or discussions that facilitate meaningful connections and learning by allowing visitors to converse with artists or other participants.

45. Volunteer

Volunteering is a fantastic way to get involved in your community, support worthwhile causes, and build relationships with people who are also committed to changing the world. Volunteering at neighbourhood shelters, community centres, schools, or environmental organisations, for example, offers a way to connect with individuals who have similar interests and values. Strong relationships can be formed while working together to achieve a common objective with other volunteers. Volunteering frequently entails communication, cooperation, and teamwork and presents chances to make connections with people from different backgrounds. Volunteering may create lifelong friendships and have a beneficial impact on the community, whether you're helping at a food bank, teaching students, or organising environmental clean-ups.

46. Join support groups

By taking part in support groups, people can connect with others going through similar struggles or life transitions in a caring setting. These groups provide a forum for people to connect, support one another, and exchange experiences and insightful knowledge with others going through similar situations. Support groups foster a sense of community and understanding among participants, regardless of their focus—whether they concentrate on health-related concerns, grieving, caregiving, or certain life transitions. Through conversing, hearing others' tales, and providing encouragement to one another, people can build relationships based on empathy and common experiences. These communities frequently provide a feeling of acceptance and belonging, enabling members to form bonds with people who genuinely get their experience. Regular attendance at support groups can eventually aid in overcoming obstacles in life as a group.

47. Join travel groups

Joining travel clubs designed for retirees or seniors is a fantastic way to discover new places and make friends with people who share your interests. These organisations plan vacations, tours, or cruises especially for senior citizens, offering a cosy and sociable environment for going on adventures together. Joining one of these organisations when you travel lets you make friends with other tourists who are passionate about seeing the globe, having amazing adventures, and relaxing. Through conversations during excursions, shared experiences, and group meals, group travel frequently promotes camaraderie and builds relationships that may eventually turn into lifelong friendships. People who share a love of travel can come together in a friendly and enjoyable setting while learning about different cultures, seeing famous sites, and forming lifelong memories, which makes the trip worthwhile.

48. Attend workshops or seminars

Attending workshops or seminars is a fantastic chance to network with others who have similar passions, interests, or professional experiences. These gatherings bring together like-minded individuals who are ready to grow, learn, and have conversations on particular subjects. Participating in workshops or seminars offers a forum for social interaction, idea sharing, and networking within a supportive educational setting. Whether it's a course on creativity, business, or self-improvement, these gatherings encourage conversation during breaks, in-group exercises, or after-session talks. Interacting with other attendees facilitates the sharing of ideas, firsthand knowledge, and insightful perspectives. This can result in the development of partnerships and connections based on common interests or objectives.

49. Join or start a hobby group

Creating a hobby group is a great way to meet people who are passionate about the same things you are. Creating a group allows you to unite individuals around a common interest, be it painting, gardening, photography, or any other passion. Organising frequent get-togethers or meetings focused on the pastime gives participants a chance to interact, exchange stories, and gain knowledge from one another. These clubs promote cooperation, friendship, and the sharing of tips or tricks for the pastime. By fostering a friendly and open environment, players can form relationships and friendships based on their shared interest in the pastime.

50. Embrace social media

Making use of social media platforms can help you establish connections with a variety of people and groups who have similar hobbies or pastimes. Participating in groups or communities on websites such as Facebook, Reddit, or niche forums enables you to communicate with individuals of different origins, regions, and hobbies. Participating in conversations, exchanging personal stories, and requesting guidance or suggestions in these virtual communities facilitates the establishment of relationships with like-minded people. Social networking gives you the chance to digitally widen your social circle by reaching out to former classmates, coworkers, or acquaintances. Social media may also be used as a platform to keep up with hobbies, events, and activities that suit your interests, which can lead to new relationships with people who have similar interests.

51. Host a potluck

A potluck is a fun and easy way to gather people together for food and conversation in a relaxed atmosphere. Having a meal at your house with friends, neighbours, or strangers promotes casual conversation and the chance to form bonds over shared culinary experiences. Every attendee brings a dish to the potluck, which fosters a sharing and cooperative culture and fosters a sense of community. Through the sharing of delectable food and conversations about cooking, the event gives participants a stage on which to demonstrate their culinary prowess and build relationships.

In addition, throwing a potluck promotes understanding and connections between people from different origins by teaching hosts and guests about one another's preferences, cultural influences, and culinary customs. A potluck's friendly vibe frequently sparks interesting conversations, belly laughs, and the forming of friendships in a cosy setting focused on delectable food and companionship.

Chapter 6: Develop your knowledge and skills

Maintaining current knowledge and abilities in retirement is essential for mental stimulation, personal development, and remaining relevant in a world that is constantly changing. Participating in online courses, workshops, or other lifelong learning activities broadens one's knowledge and stimulates the intellect. Retirees can stay educated about the world around them by reading newspapers, periodicals, or credible online sources to stay up to date on current events, technology developments, and industry trends. By participating in organisations and hobby groups, as well as engaging in artistic pursuits like painting, photography, or learning to play an instrument, you can improve your current skill set and acquire new ones. By proactively pursuing learning and development opportunities, you can maintain intellectual stimulation, adjust to shifting circumstances, and carry on making significant contributions to both individual and societal advancement.

52. Watch TED talks

Retirees can keep up to speed and broaden their knowledge on a variety of topics by watching TED Talks. Delivered by thought leaders, innovators, and specialists from a variety of professions, these thought-provoking talks provide a quick and interesting way to learn about new concepts, developments, and trends in a range of fields. A forum for learning, gaining new insights, and keeping up to date with the newest advancements, TED Talks cover a wide range of subjects, from science, technology, and psychology to art, culture, and global challenges. Retirees can learn new things, pique their interest, and stay adaptable in a world that is changing quickly by viewing these speeches. The presenters' experiences and ideas will also motivate them.

53. Reading books

One of the most effective ways for retirees to maintain current knowledge and abilities is through regular reading. Books provide a wide range of knowledge, viewpoints, and experiences on a variety of topics, enabling readers to discover new concepts, get insight into other cultures, and keep up with contemporary issues. Reading improves critical thinking, vocabulary growth, and cognitive function whether one is reading fiction for exciting adventures or non-fiction for factual facts. It offers the chance to delve into a variety of subjects, historical occurrences, scientific breakthroughs, or themes related to personal growth. Retirees who regularly read books can maintain their intellectual curiosity, stay up to date on new advancements, and carry on learning and developing long after they have retired.

54. Follow industry blogs

Retirees can stay informed about advancements, trends, and insights in certain fields of interest by subscribing to industry blogs. These blogs offer in-depth analysis, case studies, and conversations on current events and developing trends. They are frequently written by industry experts or professionals. Retirees can obtain important insights, remain up to date on the newest developments, and discover best practices and breakthroughs in their fields of interest by routinely reading industry blogs. By giving retirees access to a platform for knowledge expansion, comprehension of industry changes, and staying up to date on current events, these tools enable them to remain knowledgeable and relevant in their fields of interest or specialisation.

55. Join online courses

Retirees have a dynamic and accessible option to keep learning new things and developing new abilities by taking online courses. These courses, which are provided by websites such as Coursera, Udemy, and Khan Academy, cover a wide variety of topics and are frequently developed by professionals and instructors from prestigious universities across the globe. Retirees have the option to select courses based on their interests, such as specialised fields, humanities exploration, technological skill acquisition, or language learning. Because they are flexible and let people learn at their own speed and leisure, online courses are a good option for retirees who are trying to manage their schedules. These classes offer a structured and interesting learning environment with interactive material, tests, and assignments.

56. Listen to podcasts

For retirees, listening to podcasts is an easy and rewarding way to stay informed and broaden their knowledge on a variety of subjects. Podcasts, accessible across several platforms, provide a wide range of content delivered in audio format by professionals, opinion leaders, and hobbyists in diverse subjects. These programmes address a wide range of topics, including technology, history, science, and personal development. When it's convenient for them, retirees can study interesting subjects while taking leisurely walks, travelling, or unwinding at home. Podcasts offer in-depth conversations, interviews, and analysis, making difficult subjects interesting and approachable. Retirees who listen to podcasts can satisfy their curiosity, learn new viewpoints, and remain current on trends—all while engaging in an immersive and educational audio experience. They can be access online or through apps on smart phones.

57. Join art classes

Retirees can foster creativity, pick up new skills, and experiment with self-expression by taking art lessons, which provide an inspirational and rewarding experience. These workshops accommodate a range of skill levels and artistic interests and are frequently offered in community centres, local art studios, or online. Retirees can explore painting, drawing, ceramics, sculpture, and other artistic mediums in an organised setting by enrolling in art lessons, which help them hone their artistic skills. Teachers walk students through procedures step-by-step while providing encouragement and tailored feedback. Art classes promote feelings of accomplishment, relaxation, and personal development in addition to skill development. In addition to connecting with other art enthusiasts and exploring their own creative side, participants can unleash their creativity and go on a joyful and mentally stimulating artistic trip.

58. Subscribe to educational newsletters

Retirees can obtain a plethora of information, tools, and updates on a variety of interesting topics by subscribing to educational websites. These websites provide a variety of content, including articles, videos, tutorials, and research papers, and are curated by academic institutions, professionals, or amateurs. Retirees can access an endless supply of educational resources covering a range of subjects, from science and history to literature and technology, by subscribing to these platforms such as Khan Academy, TED-Ed, or National Geographic. Retirees can stay informed, involved, and intellectually stimulated with the support of these sites, which offer trustworthy information, insights, and learning opportunities. Retirees can easily access high-quality content and receive regular updates by subscribing to educational websites, which promotes lifelong learning and development.

59. Try mindfulness and meditation

Retirees who practise mindfulness and meditation can improve their well-being, lower their stress levels, and encourage ongoing personal development in a profound way. Through applications like Headspace, Calm, or Insight Timer, practitioners of mindfulness and meditation can access guided sessions and techniques that help cultivate a sense of calm, focus, and self-awareness. Retirees who routinely commit to these practices can develop mindfulness, enhance mental clarity, and effectively control their emotions. Through the opportunity to examine ideas, emotions, and bodily sensations without passing judgement, these techniques promote emotional resilience and improved self-awareness. Furthermore, mindfulness and meditation support better sleep, more relaxation, and enhanced mental health in general, all of which contribute to a balanced and contented retirement lifestyle. Retirees who adopt these activities can cultivate inner tranquilly and maintain present-moment awareness.

60. Learning coding or programming

Retirees can explore the world of technology and creativity through an exciting and intellectually satisfying opportunity to learn programming or coding. Online resources like as Codecademy, FreeCodeCamp, and Udacity teach retirees the principles of software development, programming languages, and problem-solving techniques. Coding fosters creativity and logical thinking by enabling retirees to design websites, applications, or digital solutions.

Retirees can explore several programming languages like Python, JavaScript, or HTML with the help of self-paced courses and tutorials, and acquire industry-relevant skills. Learning to code or programme helps seniors keep current and competent in a quickly changing digital landscape by encouraging mental agility, critical thinking, and a greater understanding of technology. It also opens doors to new professional opportunities. It provides a pathway for lifelong learning, creativity, and personal development, enabling retirees to venture forth and remain active participants in the rapidly evolving field of technology.

61. Develop your Financial literacy

In order to properly manage their funds and make wise financial decisions, retirees must embrace financial literacy during their golden years. Retirees can get useful insights into budgeting, investing, retirement planning, and financial markets by participating in financial literacy programmes, workshops, or online courses offered by credible sources such as Investopedia, Khan Academy, or The Balance. These materials provide thorough advice on controlling spending, maximising savings, and selecting wise investments based on personal financial objectives. Retirees may safeguard their financial future, make educated decisions, and negotiate financial complexity with confidence if they stay up to date on financial ideas. Retirees who possess financial literacy are more equipped to manage their assets, make emergency plans, and have satisfying and secure retirements.

Chapter 7: Engage in cultural activities

Participating in cultural events after retirement provides a wealth of rewarding experiences and advantages that can greatly improve your life in this new stage. Participating in cultural events, such as going to museums, seeing art exhibits, attending local festivals, or trying out new foods, expands your mind, sparks creativity, and promotes personal development. It offers a chance to explore various cultures, customs, and artistic expressions, broadening your viewpoint and comprehension of the world. In addition to fostering social contact, cultural pursuits help you meet new people, form friendships with people who share your interests, and foster a feeling of community.

62. Visit botanical gardens

A trip to a botanical garden allows you to fully appreciate the richness and beauty of nature, and it's a calm and enlightening experience. These gardens, which feature a variety of plant species, colourful blossoms, and lush landscapes that awe the senses, are peaceful havens. You can re-establish a connection with nature, take in the sweet aromas, and be in awe of the complex beauty of a variety of plants from across the world by strolling through these gardens. It's a fun way to discover various plants, habitats, and conservation initiatives, which promotes a greater understanding of biodiversity and the environment.

A visit to a botanical garden can be used for many purposes, such as strolling around themed gardens, learning about medicinal plants, or just taking in the serene atmosphere. It refreshes the mind and offers a little break amidst the eye-catching and bright foliage.

63. Visit art galleries

A stimulating and thought-provoking experience, visiting an art gallery opens your eyes to the world of expression and creativity. These areas are lively exhibitions of various artistic genres, arresting pieces of art, and original viewpoints that spark the imagination. You can lose yourself in a visual narrative when you stroll around art galleries, where you will come across sculptures, paintings, and mixed-media pieces that make you think and feel things. It's an opportunity to recognise the skill and vision of artists, from well-known masters to up-and-coming artists, and to learn about the various cultures, historical eras, and social topics that are reflected in works of art. Interacting with these pieces of art fosters a deeper knowledge and appreciation for the power of artistic expression while arousing curiosity and promoting conversation.

64. Join a cooking exchange

Participating in cross-cultural food exchanges is a fascinating and absorbing way to experience the essence of other culinary customs. Through the flavours, spices, and culinary methods of many cultures, you can discover the world through this enlightening hobby, which also offers a platform for sharing and learning about other cuisines. Taking part in these exchanges provides access to real recipes, cooking techniques, and cultural tales from people with different backgrounds. It's a chance to learn about the origins of recipes, ingredients, and the cultural significance of food.

By exchanging recipes, cooking with others, or participating in cultural cooking classes, you can develop a greater understanding of the range and depth of world food by learning about the culinary traditions of many places. Cultural culinary exchanges foster connection, cross-cultural understanding, and the satisfaction of enjoying delectable meals filled with history and tradition. They also bring people together through a shared love of food.

65. Join Heritage Preservation groups

A meaningful and effective approach to support the preservation and enjoyment of our common history and customs is to become a member of cultural heritage preservation organisations. In order to preserve cultural heritage locations, customs, artefacts, and practices for future generations, these organisations are committed to their promotion and preservation. By interacting with these groups, you can take an active part in projects aimed at conserving historical sites, customs, languages, traditional crafts, rituals, or other culturally distinctive practices. It's a chance to lend a hand by volunteering, supporting the preservation of cultural assets, or taking part in restoration initiatives. Participating in these preservation initiatives makes you a guardian of cultural heritage, promoting community, pride, and the preservation of priceless cultural legacies.

66. Visit historical sites

Exploring historical locations provides an engaging and immersive experience into the past, providing a concrete link to our common history and the moments that shaped our world. These locations serve as living reminders of bygone times, preserving tales of victories, conflicts, inventions, and cultural development via their architecture, artefacts, and stories. By following in the footsteps of our predecessors, historical landmarks offer a unique opportunity to learn about many eras, civilizations, and the historical significance of these sites. It's an opportunity to see architectural wonders, archaeological finds, or historically significant landmarks, which promotes a deeper comprehension of various civilizations and the social forces that have shaped our present.

67. Be a part of Community theatres

A fun and fulfilling way to experience the enchantment of the performing arts, connect with people, and let your creativity run wild is to take part in community theatre. Participating in a community theatre company provides a welcoming environment where people of all ages and backgrounds can come together to express themselves via stage management, directing, set design, or backstage labour. This is a chance to find untapped abilities, polish acting techniques, and feel the excitement of being on stage, whether in dramatic shows, musicals, or plays. Participating in community theatre allows you to work with other enthusiasts who are passionate about performance and storytelling while also fostering a sense of camaraderie, teamwork, and artistic expression. Participating in these shows gives you the chance to uplift, inspire, and have a positive influence on your neighbourhood.

68. Attend Film festivals

Going to film festivals is a fascinating and engrossing experience that transports you to the world of film, providing an engaging voyage via a variety of narrative techniques and artistic vision. A carefully chosen variety of films, including independent films, foreign features, documentaries, and avant-garde pieces, are screened at these festivals. Going to film festivals gives you the chance to investigate other genres, civilizations, and viewpoints; you can also find fresh talent and creative narrative methods. Attending screenings, panel discussions, and Q&A sessions that provide insights into the creative process and the stories behind the films is an opportunity to interact with actors, directors, and other movie lovers.

Aside from celebrating cinematic variety, film festivals also promote an appreciation for societal themes and cultural narratives depicted in motion pictures. They also offer a forum for finding influential and thought-provoking stories that arouse emotions and broaden perspectives.

69. Experience Street Performers

Seeing street performances is an exciting and impromptu way to interact with art and creativity that livens up public areas. These events, which feature gifted artists expressing themselves in outdoor settings, range from music and dance to live painting or acrobatics. Going to street performances is a great way to discover unanticipated talent shows while exploring city streets or public spaces. It's an opportunity to see unadulterated, unrefined artistic expressions, frequently carried out with fervour and enthusiasm, resulting in a captivating and vibrant environment. Attending street performances fosters community connections and provides entertainment while bringing people together to enjoy art in an approachable and relaxed setting.

Supporting street performers also helps to promote local artists and adds to the liveliness and cultural diversity of urban areas, encouraging a sense of community and celebration of artistic expression in public places.

70. Explore Street Markets

Street market exploration is a lively, immersive experience that lets you take in the sights, sounds, and tastes of the local way of life. These vibrant marketplaces include a wide range of products, handmade crafts, fresh fruit, and unusual items offered by regional merchants and craftsmen. Strolling through street markets offers a chance to meet locals, converse with vendors, and find real, regional goods. It's an opportunity to peruse a variety of stalls selling everything from local specialties to traditional crafts, and inhale the fragrances of street food vendors serving enticing snacks. In addition to providing a unique opportunity to discover treasures, street markets provide an insight into the local way of life by exhibiting handicrafts, cuisine, and cultural customs.

71. Attend Spoken word Performances

Speaking word events offer an engrossing and poignant exploration of the storytelling and poetic power of live spoken word performances. These performances enthral audiences with their raw and emotional quality; they are frequently distinguished by passionate recitations, rhythmic delivery, and moving storylines. Attending spoken word events provides an opportunity to see artists share their personal narratives, social commentary, or provocative poetry in a setting that is intimate and immersive. It's a chance to relate to the feelings, concepts, and experiences that the artists share, which may provoke thought on a range of social problems, individual challenges, or inspirational moments. Attending spoken word events fosters conversation, empathy, and a deeper understanding of the human condition while also celebrating the craft of oral storytelling.

Chapter 8: Adventures in your own Backyard

Your garden transforms into a paradise of limitless possibilities and joyful moments just waiting to happen as you enter this exciting stage of retirement. Make this your own retreat where entertainment and relaxation converge. Your backyard may be transformed into a fun and relaxing playground with a little inspiration and creativity. Take in the tranquilly of nature while surrounded by vibrant flowers and lush vegetation. Organise fun get-togethers outside, inviting loved ones over for jovial cookouts or peaceful evening talks beside a roaring bonfire.

Let your inner gardener come out and grow a colourful assortment of plants; you could even start a veggie patch or design a tranquil space for meditation. Enjoy the peace and quiet of your very own backyard retreat, where you may relax, explore, and take pleasure in life's small pleasures every day.

72. Create a vegetable patch

Establishing a home vegetable garden may be a fulfilling and delightful endeavour.

Here's a detailed how-to:

- Choose the Location: Pick a location in the backyard with good drainage and plenty of sunlight—at least 6 to 8 hours per day. Make sure it's conveniently located for upkeep and watering.
- Get the Soil Ready: Get rid of any rubbish, rocks, and plants in the area. Using a shovel or garden fork, loosen the soil up to a depth of eight to twelve inches. To increase the fertility and structure of the soil, include organic materials such as compost or well-rotted manure.
- Choose veggies to Grow: Take your friend's tastes into account while choosing veggies that do well in the climate of your area. Beginners can begin with vegetables and herbs like basil and mint, or with easy-to-grow vegetables like tomatoes, lettuce, carrots, and peppers.
- Planting: Pay attention to the depth and spacing recommended by each vegetable's planting instructions. To plant seeds or seedlings, dig holes or furrows with a trowel or shovel. Give the recently planted veggies a light watering.
- Give Adequate Care: Watering on a regular basis is essential, particularly in the dry seasons. Mulch the area surrounding the plants to control soil temperature, weed growth, and moisture retention. As needed, fertilise according to the directions on the product's packaging.

73. Do an outdoor workout

Establishing a backyard exercise area can be a great way to remain in shape and take in the fresh air.

Choose a space in the backyard that is large enough for your exercise regimen. It needs to be mostly level and devoid of obstacles like tree roots or pebbles. Choose the kinds of exercises you wish to do. Cardio, strength training, flexibility, or a mix of these could be included in this. This will assist you in organising the furnishings and equipment required for the area. If available space allows, set up the exercise stations in a circuit so that you may transition between exercises without much interruption. Your workouts may become more varied and effective as a result.

74. Have a Cookout

A cookout is a social event or get-together where food is made outside, usually on a grill or barbecue. Meats, veggies, and other meals are frequently grilled over charcoal or an open flame. During warm weather, cookouts are a frequent way for family and friends to gather together for a fun-filled evening.

Cookouts promote camaraderie and mingling among attendees. It's a chance for neighbours, friends, and family to get together, chat, and just spend time together in a casual atmosphere. They accommodate a variety of tastes and preferences with their extensive menu of grill-prepared delicacies. There is something for everyone, including grilled veggies, kebabs, and seafood, in addition to burgers, hot dogs, and steaks.

75. Meditate

Training the mind and bringing oneself into a level of consciousness that promotes calm, focus, relaxation, and emotional equilibrium is the practice of meditation. It includes a broad variety of methods designed to support mental and emotional health.

Seek out a serene and tranquil outdoor setting. Pick a location that makes you feel at ease and has few outside distractions. Take a moment to study the surrounding environment. Take note of the surrounding motions, sounds, smells, and the feel of the air on your skin. Make use of these sensory encounters to ground yourself in the here and now. Set a goal for yourself before beginning the meditation. It might be thankfulness, introspection, relaxation, or any other constructive focus you'd like to develop. If it's comfortable for you, close your eyes or keep a mild stare. Begin by centering yourself with a few deep breaths. Next, start your preferred method of meditation, be it mindfulness, breathing exercises, or repeating a mantra.

76. Host an evening talk

Having a discussion in the evening in your backyard might be a fun and interesting occasion. Establish the mood first by positioning comfy furniture, such as chairs, benches, or cushions, around a central feature, such as a small stage or designated speaking area. As the evening wears on, think about adding warm lighting, such lanterns or string lights, to create a welcoming ambiance. Next, decide on an engaging theme or debate point that is in line with the interests of your audience. Make sure the event is interesting and pertinent to the guests, whether it's a book reading, storytelling session, educational presentation, or discussion on a specific topic.

Invite an informed speaker or presenter who has the ability to fascinate an audience and impart knowledge or anecdotes about the selected theme. Set up light bites or refreshments to create a relaxed and welcoming atmosphere that will encourage guests to talk to each other after the session. Last but not least, invite people to engage and participate in order to create a friendly and inviting environment that fosters learning, conversation, and community building against the tranquil backdrop of your garden.

77. Have a Bonfire

Having a campfire in your backyard can make your get-together with friends and family comfortable and unforgettable. Make sure the fire is in a safe, designated location far from any buildings or combustible materials before you start. Make a comfortable gathering circle for everyone by arranging chairs, logs, or benches around the fire pit. To start the fire, gather a variety of fuel, kindling, and matches or lighters. To guarantee compliance and safety, check your local laws and regulations regarding open fires before igniting it.

Create a cosy and welcoming ambiance when the sun sets by using ambient lighting, such as lanterns or string lights, throughout the space. Think about bringing throws or blankets for extra warmth, particularly if the night is cool.

Gather around the bonfire and invite your guests to join you. Promote dialogue, share stories, or even bring instruments so that everyone may join in on a sing-along. For a traditional bonfire treat, toast marshmallows or create s'mores. You can also prepare a variety of food or drinks to enjoy all through the evening.

Remember to be safe by keeping an eye on the fire, keeping a bucket of water or a fire extinguisher close by, and making sure that everyone is aware of the fundamentals of fire safety. As the evening wears on, treasure the time spent with loved ones by the flickering fire and savour the relaxation and companionship that a bonfire gathering offers.

78. Make a Reading Nook

You can create a calm and relaxing area for unwinding and reading a nice book in your backyard by building a reading nook. Choose a comfortable nook or spot in your backyard that provides natural shade or protection from the sun to start. To create a feeling of enclosure and shade, think of putting it beneath a tree, a pergola, or a canopy. Incorporate natural features to enhance greenery and create a soothing mood, like climbing vines, hanging baskets, or potted plants. Set up soft outdoor lighting to enjoy your reading nook in the evening or at night, such as lanterns, fairy lights, or solar-powered lamps.

79. Plan a Scavenger Hunt

With a customised nature scavenger hunt, you can embrace the excitement of exploration and the splendour of the great outdoors! A nature scavenger hunt is a lovely way to keep active, sharpen your thinking, and interact with nature. It's not only a pleasant pastime. Whether it's a neighbourhood park, a nature walk close by, or your backyard, picture yourself discovering the beauties of nature. There is a world of wonders waiting for you to discover, from identifying different plant species to identifying different kinds of birds to looking for unusual rocks or insects. Discovering items on a list isn't the only thing this expedition is about; it's also about enjoying the crisp air, taking in the calming sounds of nature, and discovering the joy of discovery.

80. Star gaze

Enter the enchanted world of the night sky and revel in the alluring splendour of astronomy! There is a cosmic wonderland just waiting to be discovered as the sun sets and darkness descends upon the earth. Step outside for a bit, find a comfortable location in your backyard or another public area nearby, and let the stars overhead captivate you. There is an infinite variety of constellations, planets, and shooting stars in the vastness of the galaxy just waiting to be observed, whether you use a telescope, binoculars, or your unaided eyes. This is more than just stargazing; it's about reflecting on the secrets of space, experiencing awe-inspiring beauty above us, and feeling a sense of wonder and connectedness to the cosmos.

Get your loved ones involved, tell them stories, or just enjoy the peace of the night sky on your own. So gather a blanket and some hot beverages, and enjoy the mystique of stargazing—a magnificent cosmic voyage is waiting for you to explore!

81. Bird watch

Enter the fascinating realm of birdwatching and become engrossed in the splendours of nature's feathered beauties! Take a seat comfortably and your binoculars outside to discover the captivating songs and brilliant feathers of our avian companions. Every setting—your backyard, a neighbouring park, or a nature reserve—offers a different chance to observe the amazing world of birds.

Let yourself be mesmerised by the songbirds' melodies, the mighty raptors' exquisite flight, or the vibrant displays of cardinals and finches. Seek out distinguishing features, pay attention to their actions, and enjoy the variety of personalities that they possess. Birdwatching is more than only identifying various species; it's also a way to experience the tranquilly of nature and gain knowledge about ecosystems.

Chapter 9: Pamper yourself

As you begin this beautiful chapter of retirement, please keep in mind the value of pampering and self-care. This is the ideal moment to prioritise your well-being and engage in enjoyable and relaxing activities after years of hard work and devotion. Self-care is a universal need that enables us to revitalise our bodies, brains, and spirits. It is gender-neutral.

Treating oneself is not just a luxury but also a necessary component of living a long and healthy life. Give yourself a treat and indulge in the things that make you happy, whether it's long walks in the park, a lifetime of your favourite pastime, or making time to discover new interests.

Think about making time for a spa day, getting a massage, taking a relaxing bubble bath, or just relaxing with a good book and a cup of tea. Take time to relax, meditate, do yoga, or listen to soothing music—do anything that helps you find inner peace.

Additionally, make no qualms about spending money on your health—regular checkups, a balanced diet, exercise, and adequate sleep are all essential components of self-care that lead to a happy retirement.

Recall that taking care of oneself is not selfish; rather, it is a need that allows you to be your best self. Take advantage of this chance to treat yourself, value your health, and enjoy the small joys that come with retirement. t's a chance to prioritize yourself, embrace your uniqueness, and treat yourself to something special that brings a smile to your face.

82. Have a day of Digital detox

A digital detox day is when people purposefully unplug from technology and gadgets to improve their mental health and feel more present in the real world.

Establish specific goals for your day of digital detoxification first. Choose how long the cleanse will last—a whole day or just a few hours—as well as the things you'll do in that time. Set aside particular rooms or sections of your house as tech-free zones. Put electronics out of sight to reduce the urge to check them. Switch off all of your electronic devices, including your laptop, tablet, and smartphone. To resist the impulse to check them on a whim, think about storing them in a different room or drawer.

Notify friends, relatives, or co-workers that you will not be available by phone.

83. Take a nap

There are several scientifically demonstrated advantages of napping, even for little periods of time, for both physical and mental well-being.

It's important to remember that the advantages of naps might vary depending on when and for how long they are taken. While lengthier naps, especially those that begin to enter deep sleep stages, may result in sleep inertia or a disoriented feeling upon waking, shorter naps, lasting roughly 10 to 30 minutes, typically provide the benefits of greater alertness without creating grogginess.

Here are a few of the main advantages that are backed by study from science:

- Increased Alertness and Performance: Research has indicated that napping improves alertness, performance, and cognitive function. A quick nap, usually lasting ten to thirty minutes, can help fight weariness and increase focus and productivity by restoring brain clarity.
- Enhanced Learning and Memory: Sleeping helps to consolidate memories, making information easier to remember and retain. According to studies, naps—especially longer ones that involve rapid eye movement, or REM—may improve learning and memory retention.
- Stress Reduction: By lowering cortisol levels—the hormone linked to stress—napping has the

potential to reduce stress. A nap can ease tension, encourage relaxation, and assist the body relax, all of which are beneficial to general wellbeing.

- Mood Enhancement: Research has connected brief naps to improved mood and emotional stability. Napping reduces irritability, strengthens emotional resilience, lifts the spirits, and fosters a more optimistic perspective.

84. Schedule time at a spa

As you set out on this wonderful adventure of retirement, I strongly advise you to plan a spa day so you may treat yourself to some much-needed rest and pampering. After years of hard labour, this self-care day provides a haven of peace and quiet where you can relax and revitalise. Imagine indulging in opulent massages, facials, and body therapies that will not only relax your body but also uplift your soul while you're surrounded by calming scents. A spa day is more than simply self-indulgence; it's a chance to commemorate this new phase of your life by giving yourself a day of total indulgence and relaxation. Savour this self-care session that's all about celebrating you, embrace the calm, and replenish your batteries. You merit it!

85. Treat yourself to some shopping

One of the best ways to take care of yourself and practise self-care is to treat yourself to a shopping spree. Shopping is an opportunity to show your particular style, increase your confidence, and invest in your happiness rather than just purchasing material goods. Investing in new clothes, accessories, or joy-filled products can have a favourable effect on your self-esteem and overall attitude. You can express your uniqueness, learn about new trends, and explore your tastes while you purchase. It also provides a change of pace from your usual activities, enabling you to have a relaxing and pleasurable experience. A shopping spree may be an expression of self-expression, making you feel good about yourself and promoting a sense of fulfillment—whether it's treating yourself to something you want or discovering great finds at reasonable prices.

86. Practice self-affirmations

Making self-affirmations a habit is a great method to take care of yourself and practise self-care. Speaking to yourself positively can help you develop a resilient, self-empowered, and self-worth mindset. Reminding yourself of your potential, qualities, and abilities with affirmations works to dispel self-doubt and negative ideas. Rephrasing statements like "I am capable," "I am worthy," or "I believe in myself" can help you reset your perspective, increase your self-assurance, and cultivate a more positive approach on life. These affirmations are effective techniques for overcoming self-limiting ideas and developing feelings of acceptance and compassion for oneself.

Adopting self-affirmations promotes a deeper feeling of self-understanding, self-love, and ultimately supports your general well-being. It's not simply about thinking positively. Regular affirmation practice is a significant way to treat oneself with kindness and care, creating a good self-image that permeates all area of your life.

87. Buy yourself flowers

Getting a bouquet of fresh flowers is a lovely way to reward yourself and a great act of self-care. Flowers have a natural capacity to improve someone's spirits and brighten any room. Bringing a bouquet home is a way to nurture your well-being and embrace the small pleasures in life, in addition to adding beauty to your surroundings. Flowers' vivid hues, wonderful fragrances, and organic beauty can inspire sentiments of joy, peace, and optimism. You may foster a tranquil and relaxing ambiance in your house by arranging flowers to encourage calmness and relaxation. Taking care of fresh flowers also encourages mindfulness, which helps you to slow down and take in the transient beauty of the natural world.

88. Bake or make a dessert

Making your favourite dessert from scratch is a great self-care activity that can make you feel so happy and fulfilled. It's about enjoying the familiar act of baking and relishing the delectable outcome, rather than just making a sweet dessert. Baking your preferred dessert lets you use all of your senses—from the smell of the ingredients coming together to the feel of the dough or batter being mixed and shaped. This procedure can be relaxing, letting you decompress and concentrate on a practical, artistic endeavour. Plus, there's nothing better than watching your favourite dessert bake with the prospect of digging in and celebrating. When your dessert is done, that first bite is a moment of pure ecstasy that tantalises your taste receptors and brings back fond memories.

89. Take a bubble bath

Long, soothing bubble baths are an opulent kind of self-care that nourish the body and the mind. This presents an opportunity to lose oneself in a peaceful haven and let the day's worries fade. Your muscles can become more relaxed and less tense with the warm water that has been increased with bubbles or calming bath salts. Let go of your concerns and diversions while you take a dip in the bath, and give yourself permission to relax in the soothing environment. The feeling of the warm water enveloping you gives you a peaceful period during which you can rest and recover. This decadent self-care routine involves more than just cleaning; it also involves pampering oneself, engaging in self-analysis, and savouring some alone time.

90. Watch a sunset or sunrise

Arranging a sunrise or sunset observation is a tranquil and nourishing experience that enables you to establish a connection with the astounding beauty of nature. Making time to see the sun come up or set is a great way to take in the beauty of the natural world and slow down. Awe-inspiring and peaceful, the sun's brilliant hues create a breathtaking visual display in the sky. It's an opportunity to be totally present in the moment and take in the wonder of nature's changes, whether you decide to get up early to see the sunrise or end your day with a sunset. Taking in the shifting hues and the transition of the sky can inspire feelings of wonder, thankfulness, and serenity.

91. Spend time with a pet

The positive and uplifting experience of bonding with a pet can have a big impact on your wellbeing. Having a pet, whether it be feathered, cuddly, or furry, can be incredibly uplifting and reassuring. Pets provide unconditional affection, company, and a special link that can uplift your emotions and reduce stress. Whether you're playing, snuggling, walking, or just spending time together, spending time with your pet encourages a sense of connection and satisfaction. Their kind nature or amusing antics can infuse your day with joy, calmness, and a feeling of direction. Pets can also be excellent listeners and sources of solace in stressful or lonely times.

Chapter 10: Give back to society

Contributing to society is important in many ways, particularly in retirement when people move into a new stage of life. A notion found in Greek mythology is called "philanthropia," which means "love for mankind." This idea highlights the value of contributing to the well-being of people and society at large and reflects the giving back spirit.

Retirement is a great opportunity to get involved in the community and practise philanthropy. People bring with them a multitude of life experience, acquired abilities, and knowledge when they enter this stage. Using these resources for the benefit of society at large becomes possible through contributing to it.

It is important because it allows:

- Sense of Purpose: Retirees who participate in charitable endeavours feel fulfilled and have a purpose in life. It makes it possible for them to use their knowledge and experience to positively impact others, resulting in a fulfilling and meaningful retirement.
- Transferring Knowledge: Throughout their professions, retirees have often gained significant knowledge and abilities. Through mentorship or volunteer work, they can impart this information to the next generation, which advances society.

- Social Connection: Engaging in philanthropic activities provides chances to meet new people and keep an active social life after retirement. It enables retirees to meet people who share their interests and create new networks and connections.
- Impact and Legacy: Retirees can leave a long-lasting legacy by giving back. They have a lasting good influence and leave a significant legacy to society by contributing to causes they are passionate about.
- Personal Development: Being a philanthropist encourages self-analysis and personal development. Retirees are encouraged to pursue new hobbies, gain knowledge from various experiences, and develop personally.

92. Become a mentor

In retirement, one might use their abundance of experience, knowledge, and abilities to mentor and assist others who are starting down similar pathways by serving as a mentor. First, determine what domains—such as your former career, interests, or life experiences—you might draw on to help others benefit from your skills. Make contact with associations, neighbourhood gatherings, or academic establishments that offer mentorship initiatives. Whether they are young entrepreneurs, retired people, or ambitious professionals, give your time, wisdom, and counsel to everyone who asks for it. Adopt a compassionate and empathetic demeanour, paying close attention while others are speaking, and imparting your knowledge to encourage mentees as they travel. In retirement, mentoring others involves more than just passing down knowledge; it also involves encouraging personal development, sharing priceless life lessons, and making a lasting impression that will enhance the lives of both parties involved.

93. Get involved in a Legacy Project

Retirement legacy projects are endeavours that have a long-term effect and represent your interests, skills, or principles. By working on these initiatives, you may benefit the community and upcoming generations while sharing your knowledge and expertise. Take into consideration starting a project that reflects your interests, such recording local history, writing a memoir, or setting up a family history archive. Perhaps you could start a community garden, create a scholarship fund, or provide workshops related to your area of expertise. Legacy projects could be lecture engagements, art installations, or volunteer work with charity organisations. The goal is to leave a lasting legacy that reflects your experiences and ideals, influencing others and lasting long after you are gone.

94. Join a Boardroom for a Non-profit organisation

When you're retired, joining a non-profit board is a rewarding way to share your knowledge and have a big influence on causes you care about. Determine which organisations share your interests and values first. To identify a good fit, research their effect, programmes, and missions. Make contact with these NGOs and let them know you are interested in becoming a board member. Be sure to stress your qualifications and the value you can add to their cause. As a board member, become involved by attending meetings, contributing strategic ideas, and taking part in advocacy or fundraising events. Whether your area of expertise is marketing, finance, strategy, or governance, use it to lead the company.

By using your retirement for social good, you can use your skills for a worthwhile cause, make a real difference, and positively impact the community or the wider globe by serving on a non-profit board.

95. Join a Fundraiser for Seniors

During retirement, one significant approach to help and improve the well-being of older people in your community is to get involved in senior fundraising. Begin by determining which community-based organisations, retirement communities, or senior care initiatives would benefit from financial support. Work together to comprehend these organisations' needs and develop fundraising campaigns to help them. To raise money, think about planning events like community drives, benefit dinners, or charity auctions. Make use of your connections and networks to raise awareness of the issue and enlist the help of friends, family, and the larger community. Stress the value of making a difference in the well-being and comfort of the elderly and invite others to assist this admirable endeavour.

96. Donate blood

Giving blood while you're retired is a worthwhile and life-saving method to support society. Start by looking for nearby blood drives or donation centres. Make an appointment to give by researching hospitals or organisations that are holding blood donation drives. Invite your loved ones, neighbours, and friends to participate with you in this project. Giving blood can save lives, especially in cases of emergency, during surgery, or for patients in need of transfusions due to medical issues. Your contribution as a retiree can have a big effect on other people's health and wellbeing. Regular blood donation helps the greater cause of emergency medical care and public health. It also plays a crucial part in bolstering the healthcare system and saving lives in your community.

97. Volunteer at a Local Charity

When you retire, volunteering at a nearby charity can be a fulfilling way to support causes you care about and have a real impact on the community. Find nonprofits or charities that support causes close to your heart, whether they be environmental protection, animal welfare, education, homelessness, or hunger assistance. Get in touch with these organisations to find out about volunteer opportunities or stop by any orientations they might be doing for volunteers. Give your time, expertise, and enthusiasm to help with a range of duties, including hands-on support, mentorship, event planning, administrative labour, and fundraising. By volunteering, you can develop new skills, make significant connections with others, and improve the lives of those who are less fortunate.

98. Support Healthcare Causes

Retirement health-related causes are a great approach to improve people's health and the health of their communities. Start by determining which health-related organisations or projects align with your interests. Examples of these include clinics, hospitals, research foundations, and advocacy groups that focus on particular health issues. Look into the many ways you can help these causes, such as organising fundraisers or offering your time and skills as a volunteer. Think about arranging health awareness events, taking part in charity runs, or making donations to medical research initiatives. Volunteer at medical facilities to soothe patients, help staff, or support families dealing with medical issues. Additionally, you can promote healthcare legislation or increase public knowledge of health issues that are common in your neighbourhood.

99. Advocate for Social Causes

In retirement, you can use your time, expertise, and experience to promote social change by becoming an advocate. Start by deciding which social causes or issues—such as education justice, environmental preservation, human rights, or poverty alleviation—have a special place in your heart. Learn more about the cause by looking for respectable organisations, going to forums, or getting involved with advocacy groups that deal with such problems. Through community discussions, authoring blog posts or articles, or planning conversation-starting events, use your voice and networks to bring attention to these problems. By volunteering, making a donation, or pushing for legislative reforms, you can support campaigns, petitions, or initiatives that try to address social issues. You can make society more fair and just by supporting social causes when you're retired.

100. Donate to Food banks

Giving to food banks after you retire is a kind approach to combat hunger and assist needy people and families in your neighbourhood. Start by learning about the local food banks and hunger relief agencies in your community. Get in touch with them to find more about their requirements, goods of choice for donations, and drop-off sites and times. Think about planning a non-perishable food drive in your community and asking friends, family, and nearby businesses to donate food. Giving money directly to food banks is an additional strategy, as this enables them to meet certain dietary requirements or buy necessities in large quantities. You may make a significant difference in ensuring that those who are most in need of food have access to wholesome meals by making donations to food banks.

101. Join an Environmental Cleanup

One effective strategy to help create a cleaner, healthier planet is to participate in environmental cleanup projects when you're retired. Find neighbourhood projects, conservation groups, or environmental organisations in your area that coordinate clean-up efforts. Take part in neighbourhood litter-picking campaigns, park restoration initiatives, or beach clean-ups. Make contact with environmental or municipal authorities to find out what needs to be done and to plan together in order to have a significant effect. Form volunteer organisations or join existing ones to clean up your community's natural ecosystems, recycle waste, and collect rubbish. You can actively contribute to the preservation of ecosystems, wildlife habitats, and the general health of the environment for future generations by taking part in environmental cleanup projects.

Final Words

As our exploration of "101 Fun Activities for Retirement" draws to an end, I hope this book has inspired and sparked a sense of excitement in you. Retirement is a time to reinvent life, to welcome additional freedoms, and to enjoy the small things in life that make us happy, not only about hitting a specific age. Recall that this marks the start of a brand-new journey rather than the conclusion of the road. Your retirement is uniquely yours, whether you decide to take up a hobby you've always wanted to try, volunteer in the community, or just take some time to unwind. Enjoy every moment, embrace it wholeheartedly, and let everything you do serve as a tribute to the happy life you've worked so hard to attain.

This book serves as a launchpad for you to explore an endless array of opportunities rather than just a collection of tasks. I hope these ideas have sparked your creativity and inspired you to enjoy life to the fullest—that is, leisure, adventure, and the thrill of learning. My greatest hope is that you have crafted your own unique retirement experiences, moments that truly connect with your passions, interests, and ambitions, using these activities as a guide. Whether you've taken up a new activity, gone on an adventure, or sought comfort in solitude, maybe these pursuits have shown you the way to a happy and active retirement.

Thank you for choosing "101 Fun Activities for Retirement" to accompany you on this adventure. May your retirement be exciting, active, healthy, and happy.

-A.J. Johnson

Made in United States
Troutdale, OR
04/16/2024